Crazy Tired Beetches™ is a small, woman-owned company that publishes unique and fun planners, journals and gifts. We believe that cuss words can make you happy, and we are simply a group of women who enjoy laughing at life.

We partnered with our friends at Malicious Women Candle Co. to bring you a special edition of our most popular journal: Fuck This Shit Show: A Gratitude Journal for Tired-Ass Women.
Our journals, planners and calendars are designed for women to pick up, giggle, and share a laugh with their friends, family and colleagues. We are a little bit snarky, a little bit sassy, and a whole lot of fun!

We may cuss (a TON), but we find sometimes a few strategically placed F-Bombs make the stress and insanity of everyday life laughable, and a heck of a lot more enjoyable!

We are proudly based in the USA and look forward to continuing taking life not too seriously with you!

~ Kristie B (Owner), Crazy Tired Beetches, LLC
www.crazytiredbeetches.com

Part of the "Cuss Words Make Me Happy™" Series of Journals, Planners and Books by Crazy Tired Beetches™.
Visit Crazy Tired Beetches™ online: www.crazytiredbeetches.com | email us: feedback@crazytiredbeetches.com

ISBN: 978-1-950796-01-4

THIS JOURNAL OF
PURE MALICIOUSNESS
BELONGS TO

_____

DATE: _____

Asshole of the Day

Today, I'm Proud I Didn't...   Today, I am Happy I Did...

I'm Lucky To Have

Today's Shit List
PEOPLE, PLACES OR THINGS

Just punch fear in the fucking face. Then go light a candle.

Bad bitch thoughts...

My Mood Today (Rate in Maliciousness)

DATE: _____

Asshole of the Day

Today, I'm Proud I Didn't... Today, I am Happy I Did...

I'm Lucky To Have

DRAW SOME SHIT HERE

Today was infused with...

Other Shit To Remember

My Mood Today (Rate in Maliciousness)

DATE: _____

Asshole of the Day

Today, I'm Proud I Didn't...   Today, I am Happy I Did...

I was purely malicious when...

CAPTURE RANDOM THOUGHTS & FUCKERY

Today's Shit List
PEOPLE, PLACES OR THINGS

Today was infused with...

My Mood Today (Rate in Maliciousness)

DATE: _____

Asshole of the Day

[ ]

Today, I'm Proud I Didn't...   **Today, I am Happy I Did...**

[ ]   [ ]

I'm Lucky To Have

[ ]

Write
Your Own
Fucking Quote

Today's Shit List
PEOPLE, PLACES OR THINGS

JUST WAITING FOR KARMA

My Mood Today (Rate in Maliciousness)

DATE: _____

Asshole of the Day

Today, I'm Proud I Didn't...   Today, I am Happy I Did...

I'm Lucky To Have

Today's Shit List
PEOPLE, PLACES OR THINGS

May your day
go fast,
Your socks
match 3 your
underwear
not ride up your
Ass.

Bad bitch thoughts...

My Mood Today (Rate in Maliciousness)

DATE: _____

Asshole of the Day

Today, I'm Proud I Didn't...   Today, I am Happy I Did...

I was purely malicious when...

CAPTURE RANDOM THOUGHTS & FUCKERY

Today's Shit List
PEOPLE, PLACES OR THINGS

Today was infused with...

My Mood Today (Rate in Maliciousness)

DATE: _____

Asshole of the Day

```
┌─────────────────────────────────────┐
│                                     │
│                                     │
│                                     │
│                                     │
│                                     │
└─────────────────────────────────────┘
```

Today, I'm Proud I Didn't...   Today, I am Happy I Did...

```
┌──────────────────┐   ┌──────────────────┐
│                  │   │                  │
│                  │   │                  │
│                  │   │                  │
│                  │   │                  │
│                  │   │                  │
└──────────────────┘   └──────────────────┘
```

I'm Lucky To Have

```
┌─────────────────────────────────────┐
│                                     │
│                                     │
│                                     │
│                                     │
│                                     │
└─────────────────────────────────────┘
```

Today's Shit List
PEOPLE, PLACES OR THINGS

JUST WAITING FOR KARMA

My Mood Today (Rate in Maliciousness)

DATE: _____

Asshole of the Day

Today, I'm Proud I Didn't...   Today, I am Happy I Did...

I'm Lucky To Have

Today's Shit List
PEOPLE, PLACES OR THINGS

Revenge is not in my plans. You'll fuck yourself on your own.

Bad bitch thoughts...

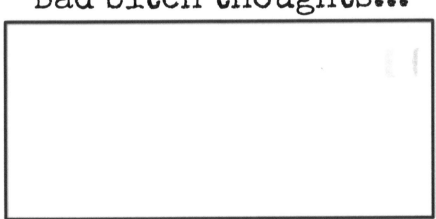

My Mood Today (Rate in Maliciousness)

DATE: _____

Asshole of the Day

Today, I'm Proud I Didn't...   Today, I am Happy I Did...

I'm Lucky To Have

DRAW SOME SHIT HERE

Today was infused with...

Other Shit To Remember

My Mood Today (Rate in Maliciousness)

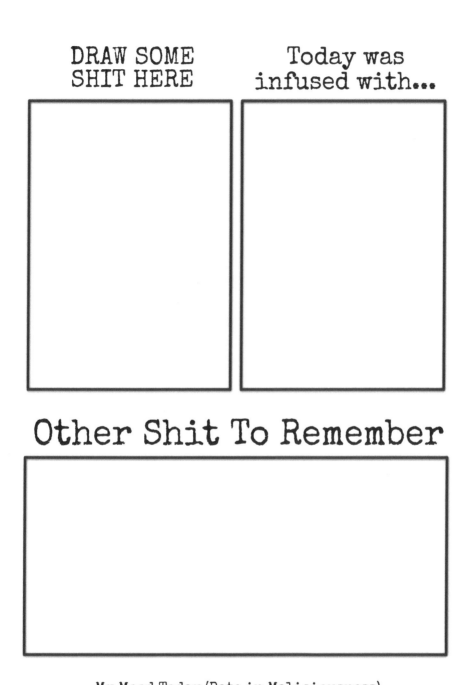

DATE: _____

Asshole of the Day

Today, I'm Proud I Didn't...   Today, I am Happy I Did...

I was purely malicious when...

CAPTURE RANDOM THOUGHTS & FUCKERY

Today's Shit List
PEOPLE, PLACES OR THINGS

Today was infused with...

My Mood Today (Rate in Maliciousness)

DATE: _____

Asshole of the Day

Today, I'm Proud I Didn't...   Today, I am Happy I Did...

I'm Lucky To Have

Write Your Own Fucking Quote

Today's Shit List
PEOPLE, PLACES OR THINGS

JUST WAITING FOR KARMA

My Mood Today (Rate in Maliciousness)

DATE: _____

Asshole of the Day

_____

Today, I'm Proud I Didn't...   Today, I am Happy I Did...

I'm Lucky To Have

Today's Shit List
PEOPLE, PLACES OR THINGS

Can you see the 'Fuck you' in my Smile?

Bad bitch thoughts...

My Mood Today (Rate in Maliciousness)

DATE: _____

Asshole of the Day

Today, I'm Proud I Didn't...

Today, I am Happy I Did...

I'm Lucky To Have

DRAW SOME SHIT HERE

Today was infused with...

Other Shit To Remember

My Mood Today (Rate in Maliciousness)

DATE: _____

Asshole of the Day

Today, I'm Proud I Didn't...   Today, I am Happy I Did...

I was purely malicious when...

CAPTURE RANDOM THOUGHTS & FUCKERY

Today's Shit List
PEOPLE, PLACES OR THINGS

Today was infused with...

My Mood Today (Rate in Maliciousness)

DATE: _____

Asshole of the Day

Today, I'm Proud I Didn't...   Today, I am Happy I Did...

I'm Lucky To Have

Write
Your Own
Fucking Quote

Today's Shit List
PEOPLE, PLACES OR THINGS

JUST WAITING FOR KARMA

My Mood Today (Rate in Maliciousness)

DATE: _____

Asshole of the Day

Today, I'm Proud I Didn't...   Today, I am Happy I Did...

I'm Lucky To Have

Today's Shit List
PEOPLE, PLACES OR THINGS

Just chuck it into the Fuck it bucket and move on

Bad bitch thoughts...

My Mood Today (Rate in Maliciousness)

DATE: _____

Asshole of the Day

Today, I'm Proud I Didn't...   Today, I am Happy I Did...

I'm Lucky To Have

DRAW SOME SHIT HERE

Today was infused with...

Other Shit To Remember

My Mood Today (Rate in Maliciousness)

DATE: _____

Asshole of the Day

[ ]

Today, I'm Proud I Didn't...   Today, I am Happy I Did...

[ ]   [ ]

I was purely malicious when...

[ ]

CAPTURE RANDOM THOUGHTS & FUCKERY

Today's Shit List
PEOPLE, PLACES OR THINGS

Today was infused with...

My Mood Today (Rate in Maliciousness)

DATE: _____

Asshole of the Day

Today, I'm Proud I Didn't...   Today, I am Happy I Did...

I'm Lucky To Have

Write
Your Own
Fucking Quote

Today's Shit List
PEOPLE, PLACES OR THINGS

JUST WAITING FOR KARMA

My Mood Today (Rate in Maliciousness)

DATE: _____

Asshole of the Day

Today, I'm Proud I Didn't...   Today, I am Happy I Did...

I'm Lucky To Have

Today's Shit List
PEOPLE, PLACES OR THINGS

When in doubt,
remember
F I S H
'Fuck it
Shit Happens'

Bad bitch thoughts...

My Mood Today (Rate in Maliciousness)

DATE: _____

Asshole of the Day

Today, I'm Proud I Didn't...   Today, I am Happy I Did...

I'm Lucky To Have

DRAW SOME SHIT HERE

Today was infused with...

Other Shit To Remember

DATE: _____

Asshole of the Day

Today, I'm Proud I Didn't...

Today, I am Happy I Did...

I was purely malicious when...

CAPTURE RANDOM THOUGHTS & FUCKERY

Today's Shit List
PEOPLE, PLACES OR THINGS

Today was infused with...

My Mood Today (Rate in Maliciousness)

DATE: _____

Asshole of the Day

Today, I'm Proud I Didn't...   Today, I am Happy I Did...

I'm Lucky To Have

Write Your Own Fucking Quote

Today's Shit List
PEOPLE, PLACES OR THINGS

JUST WAITING FOR KARMA

My Mood Today (Rate in Maliciousness)

DATE: _____

Asshole of the Day

```
┌─────────────────────────────────────────┐
│                                         │
│                                         │
│                                         │
│                                         │
└─────────────────────────────────────────┘
```

Today, I'm Proud I Didn't...   Today, I am Happy I Did...

```
┌──────────────────┐  ┌──────────────────┐
│                  │  │                  │
│                  │  │                  │
│                  │  │                  │
│                  │  │                  │
│                  │  │                  │
└──────────────────┘  └──────────────────┘
```

I'm Lucky To Have

```
┌─────────────────────────────────────────┐
│                                         │
│                                         │
│                                         │
│                                         │
│                                         │
└─────────────────────────────────────────┘
```

Today's Shit List
PEOPLE, PLACES OR THINGS

It's better
to be
full of wine
than
full of shit

Bad bitch thoughts...

My Mood Today (Rate in Maliciousness)

DATE: _____

Asshole of the Day

Today, I'm Proud I Didn't...   Today, I am Happy I Did...

I'm Lucky To Have

DRAW SOME
SHIT HERE

Today was
infused with...

Other Shit To Remember

My Mood Today (Rate in Maliciousness)

DATE: _____

Asshole of the Day

Today, I'm Proud I Didn't...   Today, I am Happy I Did...

I was purely malicious when...

CAPTURE RANDOM THOUGHTS & FUCKERY

Today's Shit List
PEOPLE, PLACES OR THINGS

Today was infused with...

My Mood Today (Rate in Maliciousness)

DATE: _____

Asshole of the Day

Today, I'm Proud I Didn't...   Today, I am Happy I Did...

I'm Lucky To Have

Write Your Own Fucking Quote

Today's Shit List
PEOPLE, PLACES OR THINGS

JUST WAITING FOR KARMA

My Mood Today (Rate in Maliciousness)

DATE: _____

Asshole of the Day

Today, I'm Proud I Didn't...   Today, I am Happy I Did...

I'm Lucky To Have

Today's Shit List
PEOPLE, PLACES OR THINGS

I run entirely on coffee and inappropriate thoughts.

Bad bitch thoughts...

My Mood Today (Rate in Maliciousness)

DATE: _____

Asshole of the Day

Today, I'm Proud I Didn't...   Today, I am Happy I Did...

I'm Lucky To Have

DRAW SOME SHIT HERE

Today was infused with...

Other Shit To Remember

My Mood Today (Rate in Maliciousness)

DATE: _____

Asshole of the Day

Today, I'm Proud I Didn't...

Today, I am Happy I Did...

I was purely malicious when...

CAPTURE RANDOM THOUGHTS & FUCKERY

Today's Shit List
PEOPLE, PLACES OR THINGS

Today was infused with...

My Mood Today (Rate in Maliciousness)

DATE: _____

Asshole of the Day

Today, I'm Proud I Didn't...   Today, I am Happy I Did...

I'm Lucky To Have

Write Your Own Fucking Quote

Today's Shit List
PEOPLE, PLACES OR THINGS

JUST WAITING FOR KARMA

My Mood Today (Rate in Maliciousness)

DATE: _____

Asshole of the Day

Today, I'm Proud I Didn't... Today, I am Happy I Did...

I'm Lucky To Have

Today's Shit List
PEOPLE, PLACES OR THINGS

Thou shalt not judge, because thou has also fucked up in the past.

Bad bitch thoughts...

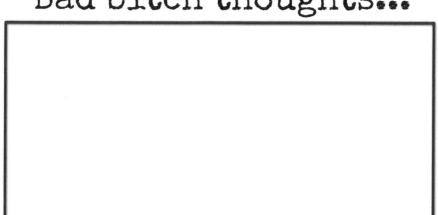

My Mood Today (Rate in Maliciousness)

DATE: _____

Asshole of the Day

Today, I'm Proud I Didn't...   Today, I am Happy I Did...

I was purely malicious when...

CAPTURE RANDOM THOUGHTS & FUCKERY

Today's Shit List
PEOPLE, PLACES OR THINGS

Today was infused with...

My Mood Today (Rate in Maliciousness)

DATE: _____

Asshole of the Day

Today, I'm Proud I Didn't...   Today, I am Happy I Did...

I'm Lucky To Have

DRAW SOME SHIT HERE

Today was infused with...

Other Shit To Remember

My Mood Today (Rate in Maliciousness)

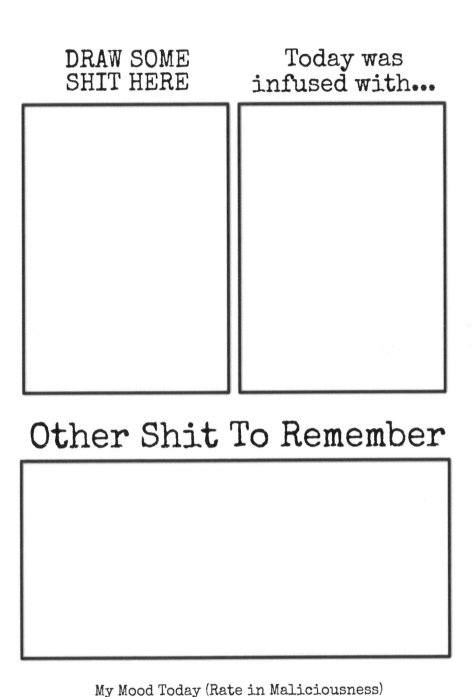

DATE: _____

Asshole of the Day

Today, I'm Proud I Didn't...   Today, I am Happy I Did...

I'm Lucky To Have

Today's Shit List
PEOPLE, PLACES OR THINGS

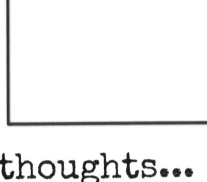

Light a candle.
Turn on the radio.
Inhale the
Good Shit.
Exhale the
Bullshit

Bad bitch thoughts...

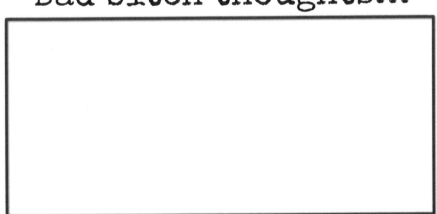

My Mood Today (Rate in Maliciousness)

DATE: _____

Asshole of the Day

Today, I'm Proud I Didn't...   Today, I am Happy I Did...

I was purely malicious when...

CAPTURE RANDOM THOUGHTS & FUCKERY

Today's Shit List
PEOPLE, PLACES OR THINGS

Today was infused with...

My Mood Today (Rate in Maliciousness)

DATE: _____

Asshole of the Day

Today, I'm Proud I Didn't...   Today, I am Happy I Did...

I'm Lucky To Have

Write Your Own Fucking Quote

Today's Shit List
PEOPLE, PLACES OR THINGS

JUST WAITING FOR KARMA

My Mood Today (Rate in Maliciousness)

DATE: _____

Asshole of the Day

Today, I'm Proud I Didn't...   Today, I am Happy I Did...

I'm Lucky To Have

Today's Shit List
PEOPLE, PLACES OR THINGS

I'm smiling Because I know Karma Will bitch-slap you eventually.

Bad bitch thoughts...

My Mood Today (Rate in Maliciousness)

DATE: _____

Asshole of the Day

Today, I'm Proud I Didn't...   Today, I am Happy I Did...

I'm Lucky To Have

DRAW SOME SHIT HERE

Today was infused with...

Other Shit To Remember

My Mood Today (Rate in Maliciousness)

DATE: _____

Asshole of the Day

Today, I'm Proud I Didn't...   Today, I am Happy I Did...

I'm Lucky To Have

Write Your Own Fucking Quote

Today's Shit List
PEOPLE, PLACES OR THINGS

JUST WAITING FOR KARMA

My Mood Today (Rate in Maliciousness)

DATE: _____

Asshole of the Day

Today, I'm Proud I Didn't...   Today, I am Happy I Did...

I'm Lucky To Have

Today's Shit List
PEOPLE, PLACES OR THINGS

Sometimes I wish I was an octopus — So I could slap eight people at once.

Bad bitch thoughts...

My Mood Today (Rate in Maliciousness)

DATE: _____

Asshole of the Day

Today, I'm Proud I Didn't...   Today, I am Happy I Did...

I was purely malicious when...

CAPTURE RANDOM THOUGHTS & FUCKERY

Today's Shit List
PEOPLE, PLACES OR THINGS

Today was infused with...

My Mood Today (Rate in Maliciousness)

DATE: _____

Asshole of the Day

Today, I'm Proud I Didn't...   Today, I am Happy I Did...

I'm Lucky To Have

DRAW SOME SHIT HERE

Today was infused with...

Other Shit To Remember

My Mood Today (Rate in Maliciousness)

DATE: _____

Asshole of the Day

Today, I'm Proud I Didn't...   Today, I am Happy I Did...

I'm Lucky To Have

Today's Shit List
PEOPLE, PLACES OR THINGS

Little girls cry. Big girls say fuck.

Bad bitch thoughts...

My Mood Today (Rate in Maliciousness)

DATE: _____

Asshole of the Day

Today, I'm Proud I Didn't...   **Today, I am Happy I Did...**

I'm Lucky To Have

DRAW SOME SHIT HERE

Today was infused with...

Other Shit To Remember

My Mood Today (Rate in Maliciousness)

DATE: _____

Asshole of the Day

Today, I'm Proud I Didn't...

Today, I am Happy I Did...

I was purely malicious when...

CAPTURE RANDOM THOUGHTS & FUCKERY

Today's Shit List
PEOPLE, PLACES OR THINGS

Today was infused with...

My Mood Today (Rate in Maliciousness)

DATE: _____

Asshole of the Day

Today, I'm Proud I Didn't...   Today, I am Happy I Did...

I'm Lucky To Have

Write Your Own Fucking Quote

Today's Shit List
PEOPLE, PLACES OR THINGS

JUST WAITING FOR KARMA

My Mood Today (Rate in Maliciousness)

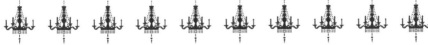

DATE: _____

Asshole of the Day

Today, I'm Proud I Didn't...   Today, I am Happy I Did...

I'm Lucky To Have

Today's Shit List
PEOPLE, PLACES OR THINGS

> I don't do the calm thing. I do the break shit and spew profanity thing.

Bad bitch thoughts...

My Mood Today (Rate in Maliciousness)

DATE: _____

Asshole of the Day

Today, I'm Proud I Didn't...

Today, I am Happy I Did...

I'm Lucky To Have

DRAW SOME SHIT HERE

Today was infused with...

Other Shit To Remember

My Mood Today (Rate in Maliciousness)

DATE: _____

Asshole of the Day

Today, I'm Proud I Didn't...   Today, I am Happy I Did...

I'm Lucky To Have

Today's Shit List

PEOPLE, PLACES OR THINGS

Don't hate someone for their outside. Hate them for the piece of shit they are inside.

Bad bitch thoughts...

My Mood Today (Rate in Maliciousness)

DATE: _____

Asshole of the Day

Today, I'm Proud I Didn't...   Today, I am Happy I Did...

I was purely malicious when...

CAPTURE RANDOM THOUGHTS & FUCKERY

Today's Shit List
PEOPLE, PLACES OR THINGS

Today was infused with...

My Mood Today (Rate in Maliciousness)

DATE: _____

Asshole of the Day

Today, I'm Proud I Didn't...

Today, I am Happy I Did...

I'm Lucky To Have

Today's Shit List
PEOPLE, PLACES OR THINGS

Life is short. Do lots of shit that matters.

Bad bitch thoughts...

My Mood Today (Rate in Maliciousness)

DATE: _____

Asshole of the Day

Today, I'm Proud I Didn't...   Today, I am Happy I Did...

I'm Lucky To Have

Write Your Own Fucking Quote

Today's Shit List
PEOPLE, PLACES OR THINGS

JUST WAITING FOR KARMA

My Mood Today (Rate in Maliciousness)

DATE: _____

Asshole of the Day

```
┌─────────────────────────────────────┐
│                                     │
│                                     │
│                                     │
│                                     │
└─────────────────────────────────────┘
```

Today, I'm Proud I Didn't...   Today, I am Happy I Did...

```
┌──────────────────┐    ┌──────────────────────┐
│                  │    │                      │
│                  │    │                      │
│                  │    │                      │
│                  │    │                      │
│                  │    │                      │
└──────────────────┘    └──────────────────────┘
```

I'm Lucky To Have

```
┌─────────────────────────────────────┐
│                                     │
│                                     │
│                                     │
│                                     │
│                                     │
└─────────────────────────────────────┘
```

Today's Shit List
PEOPLE, PLACES OR THINGS

When something doesn't go as planned in life, Yell 'plot twist, bitch!' and move on

Bad bitch thoughts...

My Mood Today (Rate in Maliciousness)

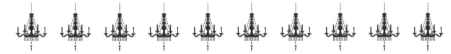

DATE: _____

Asshole of the Day

```
┌──────────────────────────────────┐
│                                  │
│                                  │
│                                  │
│                                  │
│                                  │
└──────────────────────────────────┘
```

Today, I'm Proud I Didn't...   Today, I am Happy I Did...

```
┌──────────────┐   ┌──────────────┐
│              │   │              │
│              │   │              │
│              │   │              │
│              │   │              │
│              │   │              │
│              │   │              │
└──────────────┘   └──────────────┘
```

I'm Lucky To Have

```
┌──────────────────────────────────┐
│                                  │
│                                  │
│                                  │
│                                  │
│                                  │
│                                  │
└──────────────────────────────────┘
```

DRAW SOME SHIT HERE

Today was infused with...

Other Shit To Remember

My Mood Today (Rate in Maliciousness)

DATE: _____

Asshole of the Day

Today, I'm Proud I Didn't...   Today, I am Happy I Did...

I'm Lucky To Have

Write Your Own Fucking Quote

Today's Shit List
PEOPLE, PLACES OR THINGS

JUST WAITING FOR KARMA

My Mood Today (Rate in Maliciousness)

DATE: _____

Asshole of the Day

```



```

Today, I'm Proud I Didn't...   Today, I am Happy I Did...

```


```

I'm Lucky To Have

```



```

Today's Shit List
PEOPLE, PLACES OR THINGS

I whisper 'what the Fuck' to myself at least 50 times a day to Survive this shit.

Bad bitch thoughts...

My Mood Today (Rate in Maliciousness)

DATE: _____

Asshole of the Day

Today, I'm Proud I Didn't...   Today, I am Happy I Did...

I was purely malicious when...

CAPTURE RANDOM THOUGHTS & FUCKERY

Today's Shit List
PEOPLE, PLACES OR THINGS

Today was infused with...

My Mood Today (Rate in Maliciousness)

Malicious Women Candle Co.

We Are Malicious Women

We reject all expectations of what a woman
or a candle should be.
We are a group of empowered women.
We rebel against social norms and stereotypes.
We use the F-word- not because we are crude,
but because we can.

We Are Malicious Women
Try and stop us.
Tell us our ideas won't work.
Tell us the risk is too great.
Tell us to just accept what we have
and we will show you the power of a woman.
A Brave Woman. A capable woman.
A fucking warrior goddess.
We are stronger than the bullshit.
We thrive on your doubt - It fuels us.

We Are Malicious Women
A Tribe of like minded, kick ass women standing
together.
Motivated. Determined. Ready to Slay the Day.
We surround ourselves with those that empower us.
If one of us should fall- we all gather and pick
her up.
We fix her crown.
We are never alone because we all have been there.

JOIN US AT MALICIOUSWOMENCO.COM